616·8588 HOL

1

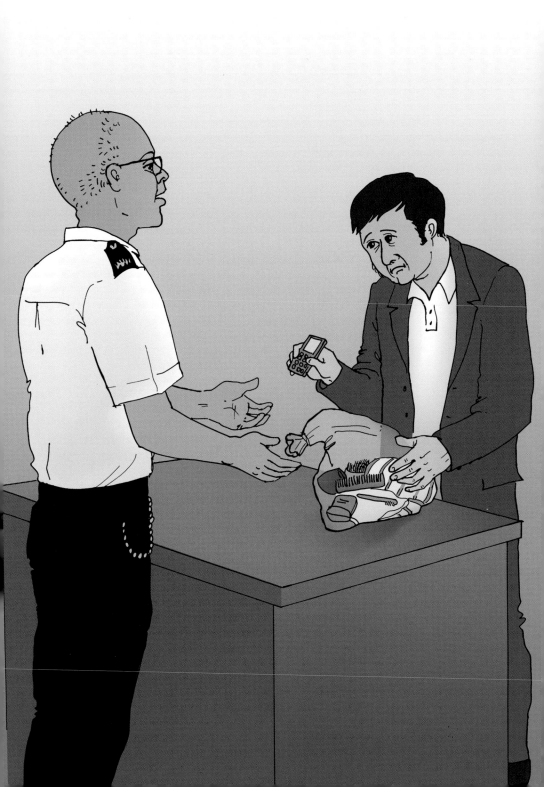

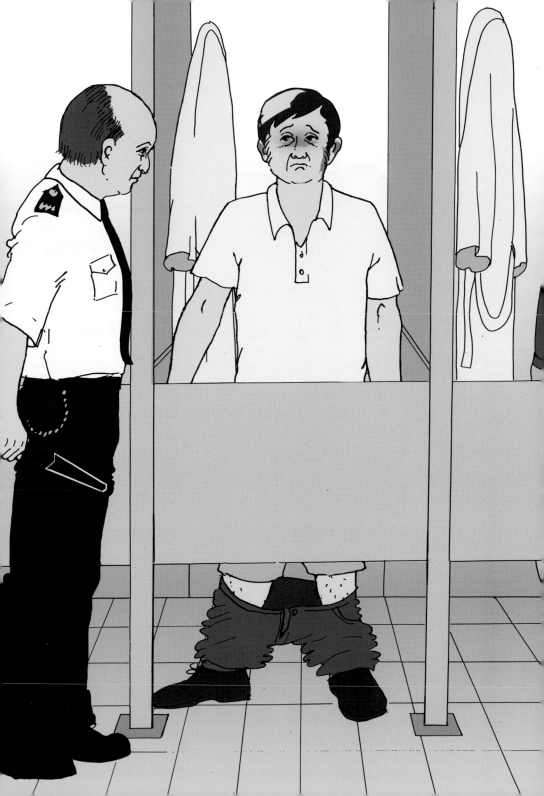

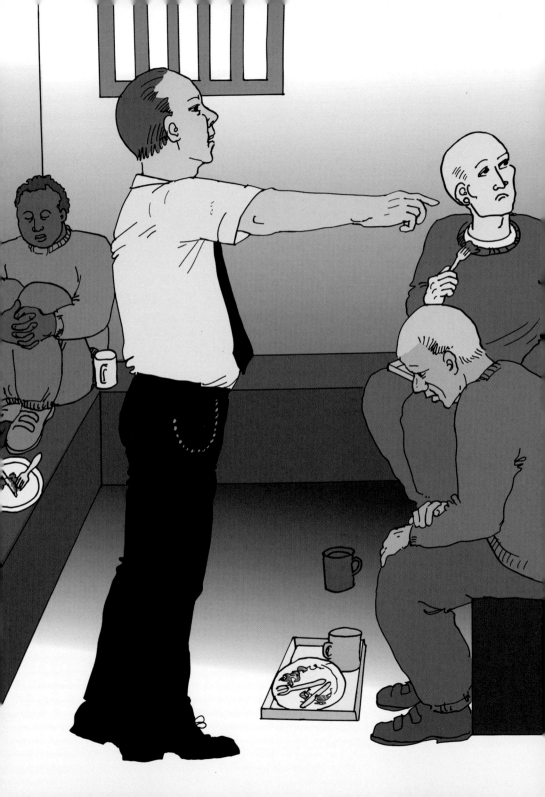

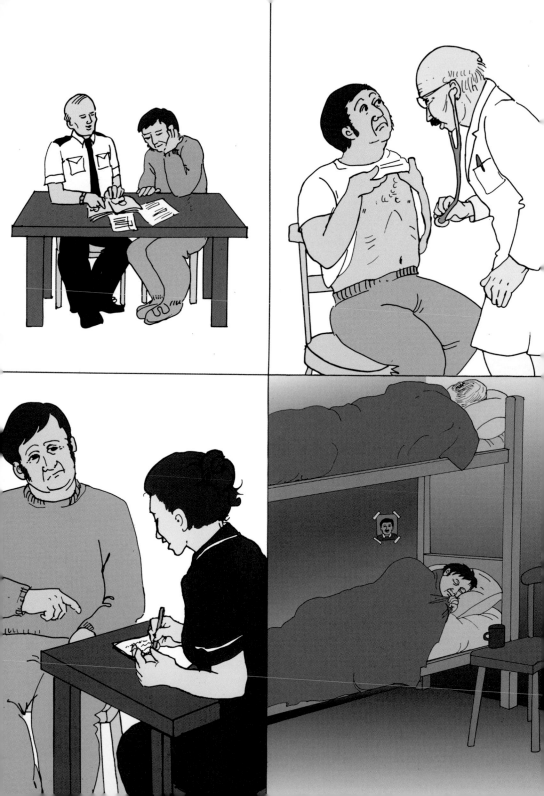

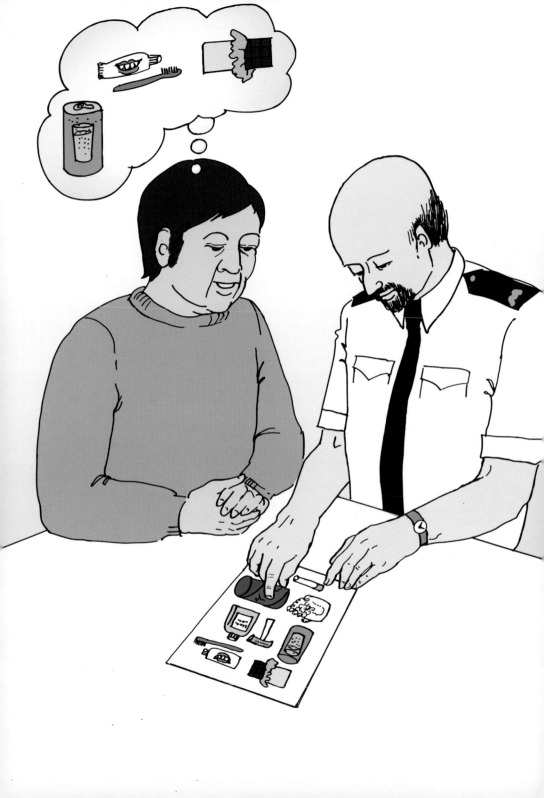

26

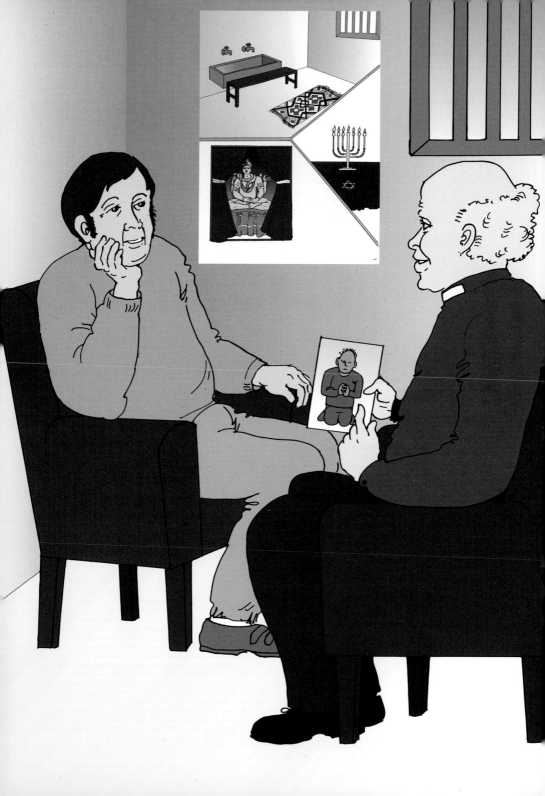

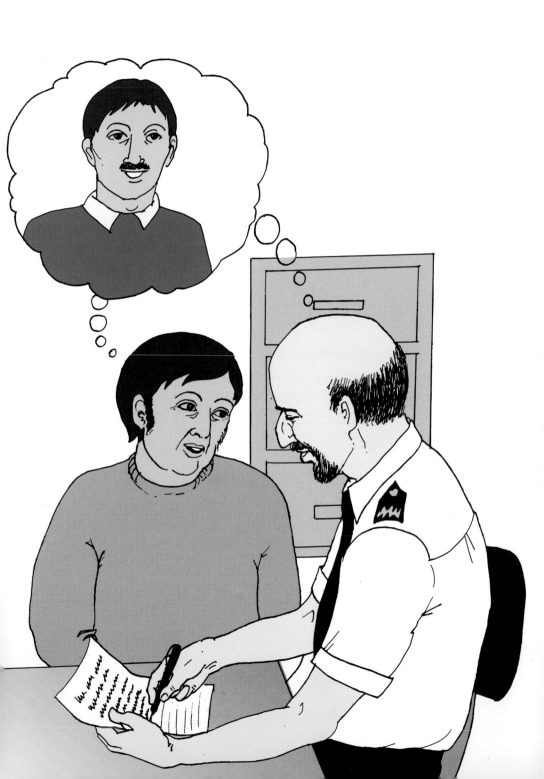

Dave's story

This book is about what happens when someone is sent to prison. Some people go to prison while waiting for their court case. Some people are sentenced by a judge to spend time in prison.

Lots of people's stories will fit this book. The pictures suit any crime. We have told one story below.

You're in Prison tells the story of Dave, a man with a learning (intellectual) disability, when he is sent to prison. The book tells the story in pictures to help people with learning disabilities and difficulties or who struggle with written English, to understand a bit about life in prison. Sharing the story with someone else, or with a group, may help a person cope with the experience of being in prison.

This book is also a learning aid for prison staff working with prisoners who find pictures easier to understand than words. It is a useful tool to help prisoners and staff to understand each other better without relying on the written word.

Words which are written **like this** with * next to them are explained in the **list of words** on page 49.

Picture numbers:

1. The prison van arrives at the prison.

2. Dave gets out of the van. He feels scared.

3. He goes with the other prisoners to the **reception***. Some are on **remand in custody*** and some have been **sentenced***.

4. He gives his personal things and his mobile phone to the staff. He wants to keep them.

5. Dave must take most of his clothes off.

6. The prison officer does a **full search***. Dave feels shy.

7. Dave gets his **prison kit***, which is a tracksuit, shoes and pants.

8. Dave queues up with the prisoners. He collects some food from the **servery***. It's a bit like a café but no one is smiling.

9. The prisoners eat their meal. Dave is not hungry. The prison officer is cross because one prisoner has drawn on the wall. Dave is scared.

10. Dave shares a **cell*** with another prisoner in the **first night centre***. Dave is in bed. It is his first night in prison.

11. Dave eats breakfast in his cell. He is with his cellmate.

12. The new prisoners all go to the **induction programme***.

13. Dave meets the staff who will help him in prison.

14. The **education assessment*** is very hard. Dave cannot read the questions. He is upset.

15. Dave fails the test.

16. Dave goes to the education centre again. Now he is getting help because the staff know he has a learning disability.

17. Dave gets a **pin number*** to use the telephone. The prison officer helps him make a call to his Dad.

18. The prison officer helps Dave fill in his **canteen sheet***. Dave chooses chocolate and a fizzy drink.

19. Dave gets his canteen. He is happy.

20. But other prisoners bully Dave. They take his canteen from him.

21. Dave has a shower. He makes a mistake by using somebody's towel. The prisoner gets angry and Dave is scared again.

22. Dave tells the prison officer what happened.

23. The prison officer moves Dave to a new cell.

24. It's better in his new cell.

25. The prison officer worries about Dave. He speaks to the **mental health worker*** about him.

26. Now Dave meets the mental health worker.

27. Dave tells the worker about the things that happened.

28. The mental health worker meets Dave often to support him.

29. Dave meets the **chaplain*** to talk about his beliefs.

30. The chaplain shows Dave where he can pray.

31. Dave speaks to a prisoner in the **exercise yard***. They share some chocolate.

32. Dave goes to the exercise yard again. He talks to another prisoner. He likes the fresh air.

33. The prison officer helps Dave to fill in a **visiting order***. Dave wants his dad to visit.

34. Dave likes seeing his dad in the visitor centre. They sit together to chat and have a hot drink and some chocolate.

35. Dave likes to play cards.

36. Dave likes going to the gym but it is hard work!

37. The prison officer talks to Dave about 'getting out' – his **release date***.

38. Dave thinks about where he wants to live.

39. Dave gets out today. He puts his own clothes on.

40. He leaves prison with his things.

41. His dad meets him at the gate of the prison.

42. Dave is home at last.

List of words used in prison

Reception: All new prisoners come here when they enter prison. This is where you will meet prison officers and nurses for the first time. They will ask you lots of questions about your health. You can tell them any problems you have.

Remand in custody: This is when the court decides you have to go to prison to wait for your trial.

Sentence: This is when you are sent to prison by the court after you are found guilty of a crime. Your sentence is also the amount of time you are sent to prison for.

Full search: This is when the prison officers search you. You take off your clothes. Officers look to see if you have hidden anything that is not allowed.

Prison kit: These are the words that the prison uses for prison uniform. You get a clean uniform every week.

Servery: This is the name for the kitchen.

Cell: In prison the bedrooms are called cells. You may be in a cell on your own or you may share with another prisoner.

First night centre: This is where you spend your first night in prison.

Induction programme: Every prisoner has to go to an induction programme when they first go into prison. It tells you about the prison rules and gives you the chance to talk about your needs.

Education assessment: Every prisoner has to do an English and Maths test. Someone will talk to you about what support you need.

Pin number: Every prisoner gets a different pin number. You use your pin number when you use the phone.

Canteen sheet: This is the way you buy things in prison. There is a form called a canteen sheet you get on the same day each week. It tells you how much you can spend, and has a list of things you can buy, for example, phone credit, stamps, writing paper, food and toiletries.

Mental health worker: This is someone like a community nurse, psychiatrist or therapist who works in the prison. The mental health worker can give you support while you are in prison.

Chaplain: Each prison has a chaplaincy team with chaplains from the main world faiths. A chaplain visits each part of the prison every day to give extra support to prisoners. You can talk to chaplains about anything that is worrying you even if you are not religious.

Exercise yard: This is a big outside area where you can exercise and chat to other prisoners.

Visiting order: A visiting order is a form you can fill in and send to the person or people you want to visit you. Different prisons allow different numbers of visits.

Release date: This is the date you will be allowed to leave the prison.

Supporting people in prison

What is a learning or intellectual disability?

Someone with a learning disability may find it difficult to understand new information or pick up new skills. Sometimes a learning disability is referred to as an 'intellectual disability' and this term is better understood internationally. Some people prefer the term 'learning difficulty'.

Many people with learning disabilities need extra help with everyday activities such as self-care, managing money and relationships. A learning disability is a lifelong condition, not an illness. Every person with a learning disability is an individual who is good at some things and not at others. Some people have autism as well, which can mean they have extra difficulties in communicating, in understanding social situations and in making relationships. Some people also have mental health problems.

What might prisoners with learning disabilities find difficult?

Prison is a confusing place for many people. It can be frightening if you do not understand how 'the system' works.

Reading prison information and filling in forms can be hard. Sometimes it is difficult to find the right words when people want to say something, or to understand what staff say. It can be hard to remember and follow instructions and rules. Lots of forms have to be filled in to apply for visits, to access health care, and to choose meals. People in prison use unfamiliar words or words that mean something different from their usual meaning outside prison.

What do we know about people with learning disabilities in prison?

We know that they need extra help but that they may not get it. Research by the Prison Reform Trust shows that:

- up to 1 in 10 adults in prison has a learning disability
- up to 1 in 3 adults in trouble with the law has a learning disability or learning difficulty that makes it hard for them to cope with going to court or being in prison
- prisoners with learning disabilities are more likely than other prisoners to be subject to control and restraint, to be segregated in prison and to be depressed and/or anxious.

What might prison staff notice about a prisoner who might have a learning disability?

Prison staff are not expected to 'diagnose' whether someone has a learning disability. However staff, and even other prisoners, may notice that someone needs some extra help.

For example, you might notice someone who is very quiet or who is getting picked on or bullied by other prisoners. They might not be looking after themselves very well. Or they might be getting into trouble for not following orders. You might notice someone who is asking for help all the time with reading information, filling out forms or telling the time. Because an application form must be completed for every request a prisoner makes in prison, this can be a good way to identify someone who finds words difficult.

What can a prison do for prisoners who have learning disabilities?

Prisons have duties under the Equality Act 2010 (covering England, Scotland and Wales) to make sure that disabled people are treated fairly. Treating disabled people fairly may mean making 'reasonable adjustments' to the way services work, for example:

- to clarify the roles and responsibilities of different departments within the prison and their links with external agencies
- to ensure that there is a system for all departments within the prison to share knowledge about a person with a disability (for example, how to communicate with them)
- to develop and agree a pathway for prisoners who have learning disabilities
- to arrange learning disability awareness training for all staff working within the prison, no matter which organisation employs them
- to ensure that easy read or pictorial information is available, for example, to explain prison rules
- to ensure that different departments, such as education, are ready to offer adapted versions of their programmes.

Reasonable adjustments may need to be personalised; for example, a prisoner who has a learning disability and is on the autistic spectrum might need a very specific plan about how staff should interact with him to ensure that all departments follow a consistent approach.

What could you do as an individual member of staff, if you think a prisoner might have a learning disability?

You could make sure the person is given information in a way that suits them. You could give them a copy of this book, and the easy read **Information book for prisoners with a disability** (see page 57). They may need help to read these materials, and in reading them together you would learn a lot about how much the prisoner understands.

You could suggest who else they can talk to, such as a 'listener' or a chaplain, and where they can get other useful information, for example, at the library.

Where can you get more information and help for a prisoner with a learning disability?

Diversity team: Many prisons have a diversity team who can provide extra support for prisoners with learning disabilities. Prisoners can put in a request form to meet the diversity team. You might need to help a prisoner with a learning disability to do this.

Chaplaincy: Each prison has a chaplaincy team who can give support to prisoners.

Listeners: A listener is a prisoner who has been specially trained by the Samaritans to listen to other prisoners. They can give emotional support to other prisoners. This is completely private.

Library: The prison library may be able to order books for a prisoner that are easy to read. They could get picture books in the Books Beyond Words series for a prisoner if they find pictures easier to understand than words.

Useful resources in the UK

Organisations to contact for help and advice

Prison Reform Trust

www.prisonreformtrust.org.uk

The Prison Reform Trust (PRT) is an independent UK charity working to create a just, humane and effective penal system. Website includes advice for families and carers.
Offenders Family Helpline: 0808 808 2003.

Mencap

www.mencap.org.uk

Mencap is a charity supporting people with learning disabilities and their families and carers.
Tel. 0845 120 2960, Monday to Friday, 9 am to 5 pm.

Services

Community Learning Disability Teams (CLDTs)

Your area is likely to have a local community learning disability team (CLDT) that supports people with learning disabilities and their families. They should know about all the local services that can support people with learning disabilities, including housing and employment.

Advocacy

Disabled prisoners may need professional advocacy such as an Independent Mental Capacity or Mental Health Advocate. To find out more about the advocacy

services in your local area, contact the Advocacy Resource Exchange.
www.advocacyresource.org.uk

UK Forensic and Learning Disability Network
www.jan-net.co.uk

An electronic network facilitated by Janet Cobb.

The Care of Offenders with a Learning Disability
www.ldoffenders.co.uk

A website created by Caring Solutions for the University of Central Lancashire to support professionals working with prisoners with learning disabilities.

Training packs, books and DVDs

Positive Practice, Positive Outcomes: A handbook for professionals in the Criminal Justice System working with offenders with learning disabilities.
www.dh.gov.uk/en/Publicationsandstatistics/Publications/PublicationsPolicyAndGuidance/DH_124743

Information book for prisoners with a disability. An easy read book from the Prison Reform Trust which will give prisoners with basic literacy skills information about prison life and where they can get help to do things.
www.prisonreformtrust.org.uk/Portals/0/Documents/pibs/Disability%20pib%20-%20easy%20read.pdf

Training and easy read resources from **KeyRing**. Offers training and materials, supporting people with learning disabilities in the criminal justice system.
www.keyring.org/cjs

Crossing the Communication Divide: A toolkit for prison and probation staff working with offenders who experience communication difficulties. This comprehensive guide provides invaluable information about different communication needs of disabled people within the criminal justice system. www.rcslt.org/about/docs/crossing_the_communication_ divide

Related titles in the Books Beyond Words series

The Criminal Justice range of picture books includes:

You're under Arrest (1996) by Sheila Hollins, Isabel Clare and Glynis Murphy, illustrated by Beth Webb. Both this book and **You're on Trial** feature the same man, Dave, whose story is told in **You're in Prison**. This book shows what happens when Dave is accused of a crime and placed under arrest. At the police station, Dave meets a custody officer and the solicitor who will help him.

You're on Trial (1996) by Sheila Hollins, Glynis Murphy and Isabel Clare, illustrated by Beth Webb. Dave goes to trial at the Magistrates' Court. This book shows what a Magistrates' Court is like, and follows Dave as he works with his solicitor and answers questions in court. It can be used flexibly for different crimes and verdicts.

Supporting Victims (2007) by Sheila Hollins, Kathryn Stone and Valerie Sinason, illustrated by Catherine Brighton. **Supporting Victims** tells the story of Polly, who is the victim of an assault. It shows her experience as a witness at court, outlining the support and special measures that help her to give evidence.

Going to Court (1994) by Sheila Hollins, Valerie Sinason and Julie Boniface, illustrated by Beth Webb. This book shows what happens when a woman is hurt by a man and is a witness at a Crown Court. It explains who she meets there and how the court works. This book is currently out of print, but will be available as an ebook.

Some other titles in the Books Beyond Words series

Mugged (2002) by Sheila Hollins, Christiana Horrocks and Valerie Sinason, illustrated by Lisa Kopper. This book tells the story of Charlie, who is attacked in the street. With the help of police, Victim Support and his friends and family, he is able to regain his confidence.

Bob Tells All (1993) by Sheila Hollins and Valerie Sinason, illustrated by Beth Webb. **Bob Tells All** follows the story of a man as he discloses that he has been sexually abused. This book is currently out of print, but is available online and will be available as an ebook.

Ron's Feeling Blue (2011) by Sheila Hollins, Roger Banks and Jenny Curran, illustrated by Beth Webb. Ron is depressed and has no interest in doing things. Through counselling and the help of his family, he begins to feel better.

For more information about these and other titles see www.booksbeyondwords.co.uk/books

Authors and artist

Sheila Hollins is Emeritus Professor of Psychiatry of Disability at St George's, University of London, and sits in the House of Lords. She is a past President and an Honorary Fellow of the Royal College of Psychiatrists. She is founding editor of Books Beyond Words and Executive Chair of Beyond Words.

Alison Giraud-Saunders is an independent consultant who helps public services improve how they work with people with learning disabilities and their families. She chairs the National Family Carer Network.

Madeleine Ryan is the Modern Matron for Mental Health and Learning Disabilities in HMP Wormwood Scrubs. She was responsible for the trial and implementation of the Learning Disability Screening Questionnaire at the prison and is involved in the Learning Disability Project Group exploring the prevalence of learning disabilities in prisons.

Beth Webb is an artist who helped to develop the concept of Books Beyond Words in its early days. She is also the author of fourteen novels for children and young people and is a professional storyteller.

Tom Ralls is a digital designer and illustrator, with an interest in promoting emotional depth through colour design and image editing.

Acknowledgments

We thank our editorial advisers Paul Adeline, Gary Butler, Marion MacFarlane and members of the KeyRing Working for Justice Group, Anthony Fletcher and Graham Keaton, for their ideas and advice about what was needed in the pictures.

We are grateful for the advice and support of our advisory group, which included representatives from HMP Bronzefield, HMP Holloway, HMP Wandsworth, the Prison Reform Trust, and St George's, University of London: Annie Bartlett, Timothy Bryan, Chris Purkess, Rebecca Skipwith and Jenny Talbot.

We are also grateful to all the people who read earlier drafts of the picture story, including Nigel Hollins, prisoners at HMP Send, prisoners at HMP Wandsworth and members of the KeyRing Working for Justice Group.

Finally we are very grateful to the Department of Health for providing financial support for this book.

Beyond Words: publications and training

Books Beyond Words will help family carers, support workers and professionals working with people who find pictures easier than words for understanding their world. A list of all Beyond Words publications, including Books Beyond Words titles, and where to buy them, can be found on our website:

www.booksbeyondwords.co.uk

You can also contact us through the following:

email: **admin@booksbeyondwords.co.uk**
twitter: **@uk_beyondwords**
facebook: **www.facebook.co.uk/booksbeyondwords**

Books Beyond Words are also available from:
www.amazon.co.uk and **www.amazon.com**

Workshops about using Books Beyond Words are provided regularly in London, or can be arranged in other localities on request. For information about forthcoming workshops see our website. Self-advocates are welcome.

Video clips showing our books being read are also on our website and YouTube channel: **www.youtube. com/user/booksbeyondwords** and on our DVD, **How to Use Books Beyond Words**.